Lots of fish

Story written by Peggy Jackson

Illustrated by Tamara Anegon

Get set! 3, 2, 1 ... Swim!

This fish is black.

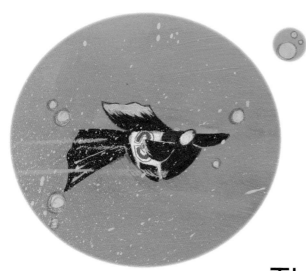

This fish is fat.

This fish has pink spots.

This fish has red dots.

This fish has long fins.

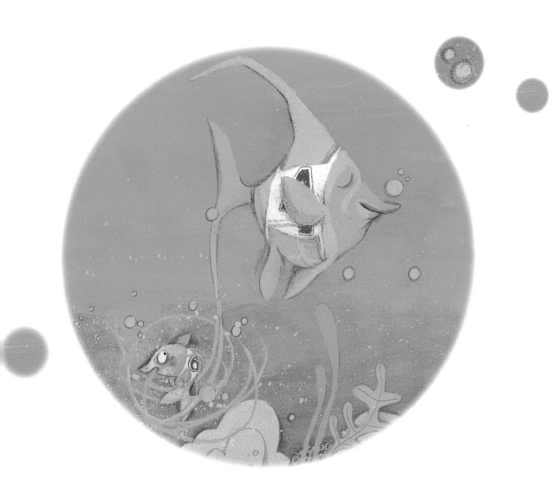

This fish is in a spin!

This fish will win!

Retell the story

Take turns retelling the story with your child.

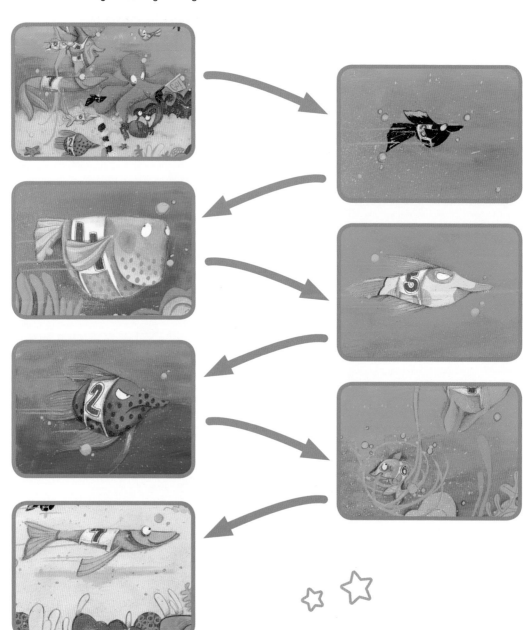